LOOKING GOOD, FEELING BEAUTIFUL

The Avon Book of Beauty

Art Direction & Design by John Staiano
Photographs by Charles Tracy

Simon and Schuster/Avon Products, Inc., New York

Illustrations by David Croland

Manufactured in the United States of America

ISBN 0-671-43062-9

*C*ontents

Introduction

To enjoy good health, to feel alive and happy, to look one's best — these are the goals of just about every woman I know. And this desire to look good is both natural and healthy.

The urge to improve one's appearance is not new. Women of ancient Egypt shadowed their eyes and tinted their nails. And we have all seen pictures of the tightly pinched waists and powdered pompadour hairdos that were the rage of the late 1700s.

But today, enhancing one's looks is an individual matter. Rigid rules about beauty and fashion no longer apply. Designers no longer dictate one silhouette to be worn by everyone, and beauty experts no longer proclaim that you have to have eyebrows that conform to a perfect arc.

Today, the mark of an attractive woman is that she is interested in fashion and beauty trends, but selects and adapts what is right for her.

Even fashion models reflect this attitude of personal style. I've attended photography sessions and seen them without their makeup, looking much like any other young women. But with makeup, as if by magic, each appears glamorously unique. Each has highlighted those features that make her special: like high cheekbones, or bright eyes, or full lips.

That is what the Avon Beauty Book will help you do — choose what is right for you. And because self-knowledge is so fundamental to good looks, our program begins in

Chapter I with a Beauty Checkup — a self-assessment and self-discovery.

As you start your program, keep in mind that making changes in your appearance will mean making changes in your habits and attitudes. That's not always easy or comfortable, but only change can get you out of a rut and ruts are boring—for you and those around you.

"All right," you may be thinking, "I'm ready for self-discovery and I'm willing to make changes. But how do I find my personal style?" This is the question we believe this book can help you answer.

As the world's largest beauty company with over a million Representatives worldwide, we at Avon are constantly asked for beauty advice.

Like the majority of women today, Avon Representatives and their customers lead demanding, busy lives. They want information that is basic, reliable, and practical. That is why we've approached the subject of beauty simply, and directed you toward a look that we call "naturalness with style."

It's all here, gleaned from our beauty experts, cosmetologists, scientists and consultants and filled with proven tips and suggestions from women just like you.

Making the commitment to becoming the most attractive woman you can be is really the biggest step. Once taken, you'll soon know that making some changes and investing some time in yourself is well worth it. It's not only looking good. It's feeling beautiful...every day of your life.

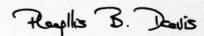

Group Vice President
Avon Products, Inc.

*S*tep into a beautiful new life

What would it take to spark your looks from good to terrific? Probably far less than you think. Often a woman needs only to make a minor readjustment in the way she looks at herself to effect a major transformation.

Think of this as a beauty checkup, as important as the physical checkup you schedule with your doctor.

Set aside a quiet, unhurried time, perhaps right after your bath. Assemble the accessories you will need for your self-appraisal session—your Beauty Time: a tape measure for accurate and up-to-date figure data...a bathroom scale...two or three mirrors—ideally, a full-length mirror and a hand-held mirror as well as a magnifying mirror. And be sure to have handy a pencil or pen and perhaps a beauty notebook.

Take time to study everything about yourself and make notes on your findings from head to toe. Look at your face. Are your eyebrows straggly? Would a little more exercise or sleep perk up your complexion? Look at your hair. Is it a bit lackluster this week? Check your arms, waist, hips, and thighs. Do you see any room for improvement? You probably will. But don't despair.

You'll be surprised how quickly you can improve your looks. Some things just naturally improve with good health, diet and exercise, while others can be corrected by beauty techniques in just a few minutes.

THE IMPORTANCE OF POSTURE

Would you like a slimmer waist? Immediately? That's easy.

Stand in a comfortable position before a full-length mirror. Look at yourself, then close your eyes. Imagine that there is a big pink balloon, helium-filled, attached to the top of your head. Concentrating on the balloon, relax and let your body go limp. Let the shiny balloon lift you up until your feet barely touch the floor. Relax as the balloon floats up to the ceiling; it will pull your body up with it, stretching the spinal cord, which has the effect of lifting your spine and your chest—but let your arms and shoulders hang down freely and comfortably as a puppet's while your neck is lifting up and away from the body. Now—open your eyes. Doesn't your waist look slimmer? Don't you look a little bit taller, better? That's good posture.

Improved posture just naturally leads to better breathing... and feeling better!

Here's a Yoga recipe for deep, cleansing breathing: Inhale through the nostrils as deeply as you can, really sucking air down into the abdomen. Let your stomach and diaphragm swell to accommodate the air. You want to fill the cavity with pure, fresh oxygen. Now slowly contract your stomach, all the way up from the pelvis to the rib cage. Force all the air up from your stomach—you can use your fingers—and out through your open mouth. Repeat three times.

"An honest sizing up of the way you look today is a must."

"The way you carry yourself can even determine whether you appear energetic or tired, optimistic or pessimistic, younger or older."

REMINDERS FOR BETTER POSTURE

■ Have groceries loaded into two bags rather than one if you will be carrying them. For best body balance, always carry an equal weight on either side. If you must carry a single heavy suitcase or grocery bag, switch it from side to side frequently.

■ Sit on the edge of your chair. Weight thus rests on the bones at the lower edge of the pelvis. This helps strengthen the back and control fanny spread.

■ When seated at your desk, keep one foot flat on the floor and elevate the other by propping it up on a thick book or firm pillow. Alternate from time to time. This is a real aid to circulation.

■ Keep your chin up and your head will follow. You'll prevent a double chin if you hold your head high and don't let your chin drop when you look back over your shoulder.

■ If your kitchen sink is too high for you to stand and work at it comfortably, sit on a stool that puts you at a comfortable height. It's better for your back, your legs, your whole body. The ideal solution, of course, would be to have the sink and the counter height in your kitchen altered to suit you.

■ To aid circulation, sit on the floor when you are relaxing. When your legs are level your body doesn't have to work so hard to pump the blood up, particularly if the veins aren't being pressed by the edge of a chair. If you are sitting down on the floor you will look more graceful if your spine is erect, weight resting on the pelvis, your legs are up with knees bent and your hands are clasped lightly over the ankles.

HEALTH, DIET, AND EXERCISE:
BEAUTIFUL ESSENTIALS

We at Avon know that looking your best takes more than good posture and better grooming. Some of the biggest changes on the outside start with some new attention to the inside. Good health will be reflected in your glowing complexion, your shiny hair, and your sparkling eyes. And the quickest way to good health is through the food you eat.

Interestingly enough, most women know these beauty foods without being told. Food that looks pretty in its raw state is also best for your appearance—cold, crisp red apples and golden cereal grains; plump tomatoes; ruddy ripe peaches; luscious grapes. Here are a few tips to better eating and a more beautiful you.

■ Collect a variety of flavors of herbal teas for quick refreshing pickups during the day.

■ Add some juice and pulp from freshly squeezed oranges to reconstituted frozen orange juice for a fresh juice taste.

■ For a refreshing drink any time, put a touch of honey and a little juice from any available fruit in a glass—strawberries are especially good. Then fill the glass with sparkling water.

■ Snack on fresh fruits and vegetables to keep your weight down.

THE PROPER WEIGHT

If your last beauty checkup indicated a weight loss is something to be aimed for, a good way to begin is to keep a diet diary for one week in your beauty notebook. Be sure to write down everything you eat or drink all week—when, what, where, with whom, and why. If you know *what* you are doing, you can change it.

IT'S ALL A QUESTION OF CALORIES

In choosing a diet, you cannot avoid the fact that calorie requirements are quite specific.

Body weight and the degree of energy output determine the precise amount of food your body needs.

Multiply your weight by 15. If you are normally active, the figure you arrive at is the number of calories you need each day to maintain your current weight. For example, if you weigh 125 pounds, you would need 1,875 calories (125x15) to stay at the same weight.

If you are very active, you can eat more without gaining weight. If you run and jog each day, swim, play tennis, or keep active in some other way for a weekly total of five to six hours, add 200 to the figure. If you seldom or never engage in sports or vigorous exercise, subtract 200.

Here are some tips to help you become a successful dieter.
1. Never skip meals—especially breakfast. It can lead to fatigue and irritability, and often bingeing later on in the day or evening.
2. Always sit down at a table when you eat instead of eating from the kitchen cupboard or refrigerator. It will make you more aware of the eating and snacking you are doing.
3. Never take a second bite of food until you've swallowed the first. Eating slowly leads to eating less.
4. Serve your smaller portion on smaller plates.
5. Make the meal as attractive as possible.
6. Let your children fix their own snacks so you won't be tempted to share them.
7. If you overeat at meals, try a small vegetable course fifteen minutes before dinner.
8. A hot drink—tea or vegetable bouillon—can conquer many hunger pangs between meals without adding calories.
9. Don't make telephone calls from the kitchen—too much temptation!
10. Keep some kind of busywork for your hands beside the chair where you watch television. Even if other members of the family snack while they watch, you can resist if you're doing some productive knitting.

Diet and exercise go hand in hand for good health, and supply that extra bounce and glow that make every woman more attractive.

With just a little increase in your exercise schedule, you can step up your circulation; and an increase in circulation provides more beautiful skin, hair, and nails.

Try to build some toning and warm-up exercises as well as spot-reducing exercises into your daily schedule—20 minutes or so before breakfast or 20 minutes before you go to bed. You'll be surprised how quickly flabby muscles and loose flesh become firm and supple.

Even more important and more fun, engage in some kind of active sport or game. A regularly scheduled game of tennis, for example, or jogging, jumping rope, swimming, bicycling, roller skating, or even dancing can provide healthy exercise and an added opportunity to socialize with your friends. Oddly enough, exercise isn't really tiring; rather, it stimulates your mind and body. In today's busy world, regular exercise can offer an outlet for tension and replenish your energy at the same time.

"All the good things you do for yourself are better and more effective if you let your body become more active."

SKIN the mirror of the b

ody

*G*ive yourself the best-looking skin

You write your own life story every day, and your skin is where others read it. Skin has been called the mirror of the body. It accurately reflects the state of your health, past and present. But you can rewrite the script, because skin is constantly renewing itself. New cells mature in approximately fifteen days, and old skin cells are constantly being shed. Skin responds almost overnight to a new program of proper cleansing and care.

THERE'S MORE TO SKIN THAN MEETS THE EYE

Thin as it is, the skin is composed of two individual layers, plus a third layer of fatty tissue just beneath the skin. The top layer, the epidermis, is composed at its surface of flattened cells of keratin, which are constantly being sloughed off and replaced. Within the epidermis are specialized cells, called melanocytes, which produce melanin, the pigment that gives skin and hair its color. When the skin is exposed to the sun, melanin production is increased and a tan results.

Below the epidermis, but bound to it, is the skin's second layer, the dermis. Collagen and elastin, the major proteins of the skin, are produced in the dermis. They knit together to form skin that has a supple, elastic tone and strength.

Glands and tiny blood vessels in the dermis nourish the skin, hair and nails, and supply the fluids that lubricate and protect the epidermis. The dermis houses capillaries, perspiration glands and hair roots. Beneath the dermis is the subcutaneous fatty tissue, which is thicker in some places than in others. Its "hills and valleys" are what help determine the contours of the face.

pH AND THE "ACID MANTLE"

Healthy skin constantly secretes water (perspiration) and an oily material (sebum), which combine or emulsify on the surface of the skin into a single substance that lubricates and protects. This emulsion makes the skin look plump and moist, and when skin and its surroundings are operating under peak conditions, it is chemically balanced to provide an antiseptic condition that kills microbes on the skin surface.

Many years ago, the chemist Marchionini researched the chemical structure of this natural skin lubrication. He used the pH scale, which goes from 0 to 14, to describe its relative acidity. Neutral (neither acid nor alkaline) is pH 7; numbers below 7 indicate acid materials; those above, alkaline. Marchionini's studies showed that healthy skin may range from pH 3.0 to pH 5.5. He reasoned that this microscopic film of acidic moisture over the skin and hair was a kind of protective covering, which he called the "acid mantle."

Your skin generally maintains its acidic mantle without special attention, provided you cleanse regularly with gentle products.

Most soaps and cleansers made for facial use are either close to neutral or slightly alkaline. Skin is instantly returned to its acidic state if, after cleansing, you use an astringent toner.

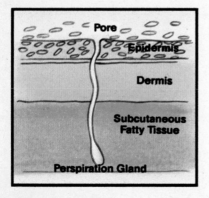

"Too high an acid level can create problems of itchy skin and scalp, and a cleanser that is too acid just won't clean."

SKIN IS MOISTURE

Healthy skin is up to 90 percent water. Water trapped within the cells keeps skin plumped and firm. But the body and the skin lose water constantly. On an average day, through elimination and perspiration, the body expels more than 1½ pints of water. So in order to keep your skin dewy and firm, "just add water." Doctors suggest drinking six to eight glasses of water a day. If that sounds boring, try sparkling mineral water with a slice of lime, or add a little splash of fruit juice to sparkling water.

Water inside your body keeps body skin plump and glowing. Oddly enough, water on the surface encourages dryness. For the best-looking skin, you must trap water within the upper layer of the skin, yet keep water off the surface of the skin. For this double task, a protective lubricant or moisturizer is needed.

Most moisturizers contain both humectants and emollients. Humectants attract water within the tissues and draw it to the cells of the epidermis to keep this top layer of skin plump and hydrated. Emollients coat the skin with a lubricating shield to help prevent the evaporation of moisture.

NO TIME FOR A REGIMEN?

You hear a lot about programs and regimens of skin care. It sounds forbidding, doesn't it? Who has time for a regimen when she has to get the children off to school and be at work on time?

Well, "regimen" is just a fancy word for a very simple but vital cleansing procedure—the 1-2-3 of cleanse-tone-moisturize, basic to every woman's skin care.

EVERY SKIN NEEDS A GOOD CLEANSING

Most of the dead cells the skin constantly sheds just fall off and fly away unseen—left behind on the pillow, rinsed off in the bath, shed as we go about the day. But some remain on the surface of your skin and hide the fresh new skin beneath. Black women are very much aware of this and know the condition as ashiness.

You have to scrub away the clinging dead cells in order to reveal younger, fresher skin. This can be done with special creams called exfoliating creams, or with an abrasive cleansing puff designed to be used with rinse-off cleansing creams or with soap and water to give the face a very minor form of the epidermabrasion favored by dermatologists.

"You hear a lot about programs and regimens of skin care...Well, a regimen is just a fancy word for the very simple but vital cleansing procedure—the 1-2-3 of cleanse-tone-moisturize, basic to every woman's skin care."

If your skin is Dry

SPECIAL NOTE: Neglect shows fast in the form of crepiness, so be generous with protective measures. Be gentle but vigilant about sloughing off dry dead cells that dull the surface beauty.

P.M. Evening first—that's when dry skin should get a thorough cleansing.

WHAT TO USE	HOW TO USE IT
1. Dry-skin cleanser:	Massage with fingertips upward and outward from throat.
Tissue-off type or	Dampen a tissue to remove all traces of makeup and cleanser.
Rinse-off cleanser or cleansing bar	Scrub face lightly using wet washcloth or abrasive puff with rinse-off cleanser or bar. Rinse thoroughly with cool to lukewarm water
2. Low-alcohol skin toner	Apply with a cotton pad to erase any remaining bit of makeup, cream, or soap.
3. Rich night cream	Protect your skin with a thin film of cream. Apply 15 minutes before bed, then blot off any excess.

A.M. An abbreviated version of the evening routine because you are not removing dirt and makeup. Also, dry skin does not secrete as much oil.

WHAT TO USE	HOW TO USE IT
1. Low-alcohol skin toner	Splash your face with lukewarm water and then cool water before applying toner on a cotton pad. Blot face dry.
2. Moisturizer	Rub a little moisturizer between your fingers— body heat liquefies cream so it spreads easily and goes further—and sweep it up lightly from base of throat to hairline. Blot off excess.

WEEKLY

WHAT TO USE	HOW TO USE IT
1. Peel-off mask and/or	Use a deep-cleansing mask alone or followed with a second mask to moisturize skin. Always apply a thin film of moisturizer to very dry skin before using a peel-off mask.
2. Moisturizing mask	

If your skin is Oily

SPECIAL NOTE: Your skin demands a lot of care and may seem the most troublesome type, but in the long run, oily skin is a blessing. Skin usually becomes drier with age, so the young woman with oily skin becomes the woman whose skin is moist and unlined late in life.

A.M.

WHAT TO USE	HOW TO USE IT
1. Cleanser designed for oily skin	If skin is troubled with acne, use specially designed products; if acne is a chronic problem, follow your doctor's advice. The gentle use of a cleansing puff with an abrasive surface helps keep clogged pores open, as well as removing excess oil and shine. Rinse with lukewarm water. Blot dry.
2. Astringent	Saturate a cotton pad with astringent and wipe upward and outward. Repeat until pad is clean.
3. A light moisturizer	Unless your skin is very oily, moisturizer will help protect it, especially the eye, cheek and throat areas.

AFTERNOON

WHAT TO USE	HOW TO USE IT
Cleanser, astringent, and light moisturizer	Refresh by removing makeup, cleansing and toning. Follow with a light moisturizer and fresh makeup, if you wish.

P.M.

WHAT TO USE	HOW TO USE IT
1. Cleanser	As in the morning and afternoon.
2. Astringent	As in the morning and afternoon.
3. Moisturizer	Only around the eyes.

WEEKLY

WHAT TO USE	HOW TO USE IT
1. Clay-based deep-cleansing mask or peel-off mask	Add a facial mask to the nice things that you do for yourself on your Beauty Time. Use either type of facial mask listed to give oily skin a thorough cleansing.

If your skin is a Combination

SPECIAL NOTE: If you are fortunate enough to have that delicately balanced skin between Dry and Oily, yours is the rare type called Normal. You should use products designed for normal skin to maintain this condition. Combination skin usually has oily parts at the T-zone of forehead, nose, and chin. Review the condition of your skin frequently for changes.

P.M. Evening first, because that's when combination skin gets a thorough, scrupulous cleansing.

WHAT TO USE	HOW TO USE IT
1. Cleanser:	Massage with fingertips upward and outward from throat.
Tissue-off type or	Dampen a tissue to remove all traces of makeup and cleanser.
Rinse-off cleanser or cleansing bar	Scrub face lightly using wet washcloth or abrasive puff with rinse-off cleanser or bar. Rinse thoroughly with cool to lukewarm water.
2. Astringent and mild toner	Use astringent for oily areas and toner for dry areas. Saturate cotton pads and wipe until pads are clean.
3. Night cream	Apply only to delicate dry areas, such as eyes, cheeks and throat, for protection while you sleep.

A.M. A quick, abbreviated version of the evening routine.

WHAT TO USE	HOW TO USE IT
1. Cleanser	Cleanse only those areas of your face that become shiny overnight. Rinse with cool water.
2. Astringent and mild toner	As in the evening.
3. Moisturizer	Moisturize lightly from throat to hairline, covering all but the oiliest areas.

WEEKLY

WHAT TO USE	HOW TO USE IT
1. A facial mask	You can use a deep-cleansing mask on oily areas and a moisturizing one on the dry areas.

EVERY SKIN RESPONDS TO
A TREAT NOW AND THEN

No matter what kind of skin you have, every skin responds to a special treat once a week, a mini-vacation for the skin that needn't require a visit to a skin salon. Give yourself a refreshing, cleansing mask right at home.

Heat water in a large, shallow saucepan on the stove. Toss a bag of chamomile herb tea into the water when it starts to simmer. (The herb is optional, but does give the vapors a soothing, delicious aroma.)

Take the steaming pan off the burner. Arrange a towel over your head to make a sort of tent and bend over the pan. The towel prevents the steam from escaping. Close your eyes and let the warm vapors play across your face. In the moist warmth, pores throw off impurities, and your skin will be quite clean by the time the water stops steaming. Lift your head, blot your face with the towel, and use your fingertips to paint on a facial mask. (Refer to the care chart for your skin type for the best kinds of masks to use.)

Read the directions carefully. Cover forehead, nose, and chin with the mask. Avoid eyes, lips, and hairline. Stroke mask back from cheeks to the ears. Check the specified time, and set the alarm or a kitchen timer. Don't leave a mask on longer than the directed time; it doesn't increase the mask's benefits to skin, and removal takes longer.

While the mask is working, just lie back and relax. This is a blissful vacation for the skin, one from which it returns with a lasting glow.

*E*ven with the most loving care

Skin sometimes falls victim to a problem. Some respond right away to a little special attention at home. But others don't. Stubborn problems, including those caused by allergies, should be turned over to a dermatologist who specializes in studying the skin and its health.

Remember, skin acts as an early-warning signal for many internal illnesses. Seeing a dermatologist for what seems a little problem may spare you larger ones. You really owe it to yourself to find a good dermatologist whenever your skin takes a puzzling turn for the worse. Ask your family doctor or the county medical board for a good skin specialist. Or check your local hospital; often dermatological clinics at university-affiliated hospitals provide almost-free treatment.

Among the most common problems are these:

Blackheads—a blackhead is a clogged oil gland. The opening of the gland is blocked by excess sebum. When the sebum is exposed to air it oxidizes and darkens, forming the blackhead or comedo. Use a facial sauna, or heat a saucepan of water until it simmers. Remove the pan from the heat and hold your face in the steam, with a towel tented over your head to hold the steam in. Then apply a peel-off or clay-based facial mask to draw out the blackheads. Follow with astringent toner. Don't squeeze. You risk infection and damaging the skin.

Whiteheads—a whitehead is composed of hardened, fatty materials that collect below the surface of the skin. If consistent, thorough cleansing according to your skin type does not help whiteheads disappear, a dermatologist can remove them. Do not squeeze: the whitehead won't come out and you risk infection.

Hives—a case of hives can be an allergic reaction, or it can be brought on by stress. Many medications—even one as simple as aspirin—can aggravate hives. See the dermatologist.

Freckles—freckles are simply little isolated islands of melanin in the skin. The sun seems to intensify them, although a tendency to freckles is hereditary. Attempts to remove them medically are futile, but some bleaching creams do help. Or you can cover them with makeup. Or best of all, stop worrying and recognize that for people who don't have them, freckles are charming.

Mask of Pregnancy—The technical name for this discoloration of the skin, usually in a butterfly shape on the upper part of the face, is melasma or chloasma. Birth control pills may be responsible. A bleaching cream can help remove it. Look for one containing 1.5 to 2 percent hydroquinone. This is the only active ingredient that is both safe and effective. Be careful of the sun. After using a bleaching cream, avoid excessive exposure to sunlight or use a sunscreen.

AGING SKIN

This is, strictly speaking, an overall skin condition rather than a specific problem. But it is _the_ big skin worry, the one that will affect us all.

There are measures to take, however, that will help prevent, arrest, correct, or at the very least minimize the apparent effects of aging skin. The first step in winning the war is to know your enemy.

THE SIGNS OF AGING SKIN (AND SOME FIRST-AID TACTICS)

Tiny Lines: Moisturize and lubricate skin around the clock to help lines from developing into wrinkles; avoid the sun and hot, dry air; stop smoking; drink plenty of water to keep skin plump and hydrated from within.

Dry, Stiff, Itchy Skin: If you are a soap and water person, try rinsing twice as many times as usual, or twice as long as you currently do when you wash your face. Use cold water for rinsing. Don't dry your face but tone with the mildest toner and apply moisturizer to damp skin. Keep indoor air as moist as possible with humidifiers, and apply body lotion liberally.

Liver Spots, or Senile Lentigo: There is no known preventive measure. However, some women have found the use of a bleaching cream containing 1.5 to 2% hydroquinone successful, but if you use this method, remember that the cream must be applied only to the spot not the skin around it. To minimize spots on the face, use a concealing cover cream half a shade lighter than your foundation. To minimize spots on the hands, avoid very dark or bright nail enamel or very elaborate rings and bracelets, which will focus extra attention on your hands.

Bags and Pouches Under the Eyes: Check with your doctor to be sure a sinus or kidney problem is not involved; sleep with your head elevated on a firm pillow; see makeup section for tips on minimizing pouches. Glasses with tinted lenses can help disguise signs of aging in the eye area. Cool gray and blue-gray tints are almost universally attractive. Brownish tints tend to make eyes look tired.

Drooping Eyelids: Skin that overhangs the lids can be made less noticeable if you keep your eyebrows light and delicate.

Crow's Feet: Sunglasses must be dark enough to protect against glare. Wear them whenever you go outdoors on bright days. Indoors, have adequate light for reading. Keep the skin around your eyes moisturized at all times.

Wrinkles Across the Forehead: You can minimize them with temporary wrinkle smoothers. Play up good features so as to distract the eye from the lines on your forehead—use eye-catching earrings, vibrant lipstick, attractively styled hair.
Vertical Lines Extending Beyond the Lips: To avoid lipstick's "traveling" or "feathering" in these tiny lines, powder your lips before using lip color, and outline the lips with a lip pencil or brush for a lasting, clear lip shape. Some lipsticks do not feather as much as others; experiment.

SPECIAL TIPS

DO protect your skin with moisturizer and sunscreens when it is exposed to sun, wind, dry heat, or cold. Don't expose your skin to any of these rough weather conditions unnecessarily.
DON'T smoke! Dermatologists find that smokers wrinkle much more and much sooner than non-smokers, because of destruction of collagen—the protein that holds skin together. Breakdown of collagen around the eyes coupled with habitual squinting against the smoke leads to heavy wrinkling.
DO use the lightest touch when applying creams and cosmetics. When applying cream around your eyes, don't stroke it on; rather, press delicately, and moving from the outer corners toward the nose.

ABOUT PLASTIC SURGERY

Any surgery is serious, and unnecessary surgery should be avoided. Yet for a woman with the right motivation and the right expectations, cosmetic surgery may prove to be a rewarding experience.

However, a prospective patient should not have unreasonable hopes. Cosmetic surgery will not help you regain your youth, but it should improve your appearance and make you look as trim, alert, and attractive as you feel.

If you are seriously considering plastic surgery, you should read all you can on the subject. Then ask your own physician to recommend qualified surgeons whom you might consult, or write your county medical society. Your surgeon should have passed the exams of the American College of Surgeons and be entitled to use the letters FACS (Fellow of the American College of Surgeons) after his or her name.

Make appointments to discuss surgery with at least two doctors. The doctors will show you before and after photographs of similar operations and will discuss your entire medical history. Be sure to ask for complete information on recuperation time, discomfort, and any possibility of scars. In general, the darker the skin, the more the skin tends to form keloids—thick, fibrous scar tissue. This makes surgery results on Black skin much less predictable.

Face-lifts are the best known operations in cosmetic surgery. The medical name is rhytidectomy. Facial skin is pulled up and back to soften wrinkles and eliminate sagging jowls. Sometimes muscles under the skin and jaw are tightened.

Depending on what is done, the lasting time for the results varies from five years to a lifetime. Costs, naturally, vary considerably.

"How you will age and how your skin will show it depends partly on your genes. You can get some idea of your potential pattern of lines and wrinkles by studying your mother's face."

*S*ome time in the sun

You know how to make raisins, don't you? Take some plump, juicy grapes with smooth, satiny skin and put them in the sun for a while. What the sun does for grapes, it can also do to your skin.

Some sun is fine. A little sun exposure is needed for the body to synthesize vitamin D. However, it takes only 19 square inches of skin and five minutes of sun a day to provide all the vitamin D you need. So be sure to protect your skin with sunscreens or blocks whenever you expect to be in the sun for more than a few minutes.

Several chemicals are effective sunscreens. The best is generally agreed to be PABA (para-aminobenzoic acid) and its derivatives. Since 1978, by law, the SPF or sun protection factor of a sunscreen must be noted by number on the product. The higher the SPF number, the greater the degree of protection the product affords.

Sun blocks prevent burning and tanning. Zinc oxide, the white paste lifeguards often wear on nose and lips, is the most common.

TIPS IN THE SUN

Don't
■ Use a sun reflector.
■ Be fooled by haze or clouds, which block only about half the burning rays.
■ Think you are safe under a beach umbrella—rays reflected off sand and water can burn you from all sides, and most umbrellas block only about half the rays that come from above.

Do

■ Wear good dark sunglasses. If your eyes can be easily seen through the sunglasses, the glasses aren't dark enough.

■ Remember that certain medications can cause skin to have a photosensitive reaction—irritation or a quick, bad sunburn—so take extra precautions.

■ Change your position frequently so no single area of skin is exposed to the sun for too long.

Sun Protection Factor Chart

Skin Type		SPF	Protection
A.	Always burns easily, never tans, sensitive	8 to 15	Maximum to Ultra
B.	Always burns easily, tans minimally, sensitive	6 to 8	Maximum
C.	Usually burns slightly, tans gradually	4 to 6	Moderate
D.	Seldom burns, tans easily	2 to 4	Minimal
E.	Rarely burns, gets very dark tan	2	Minimal

Just as you dress differently according to the weather, you must treat your skin in a special way to protect it from temperature and moisture conditions that vary from season to season.

SUMMERPROOF YOUR SKIN

Warm weather makes us feel more relaxed and active, and invigorates our skin. Cell production and turnover is more rapid, oil glands more active. All that, plus a little sunshine and fresh air, adds up to better-looking skin for almost everyone. Although many minor skin annoyances seem to clear up spontaneously, you do have to keep up skin care every day. Skin-care and makeup products containing sunscreen are especially important at this time of year. Moisturizer is most important on those days when you use almost no makeup. It protects your skin and also helps make your complexion look more even and glowing. Be sure to use an eye cream. Lubrication helps prevent crinkle lines you get from squinting against bright daylight and glare.

You can lose body heat through your extremities in hot weather as well as cold, so rinse feet and wrists in cold water for a quick refresher.

Unless your skin is very oily, don't cleanse more often, but do rinse your face more frequently with cool water; follow with a light toner and moisturizer. Be sure to accent your eyes with mascara and delicate eyeliner so they don't get lost in your tan. Use lipstick and gloss; add blush high on the apple of your cheeks for a healthy and happy summer look.

WINTERIZE YOUR SKIN

You'd do as much for your car, wouldn't you? Cold, dry air and hot, dry air are equally bad for skin, and we have to contend with both kinds in the course of a winter day. We go from cold, dry air outdoors into heat that's often as dry as the Sahara.

Before going out in the cold, moisturize well. Protect your eyes with eye cream or use an extra dab of moisturizer on the delicate skin around the eyes. You want a somewhat glowing face in cold weather, a less matte finish to makeup on winter days. Cream blush and cream eye shadows are a great idea in cold, dry weather, when even oily skin tends to be slow about producing natural moisture. Lips need lots of protection against chapping, so cream lipstick and gloss are essential.

Be lavish with moisturizer all over your body. Dry skin is a real hazard in winter, especially on hands and legs. Don't neglect pedicures in winter to keep feet comfortable and smooth inside boots. Treat your feet to cream after the bath, and follow with powder to keep them comfortable and dry (important since boots trap perspiration inside, and that's bad for the skin). Use a hand cream, and don't forget cuticle cream around your nails—it won't harm your manicure, and definitely will help your hands. For your hair, regular conditioning is a must. Like skin, it tends to dry and can actually break in freezing temperatures.

Sudden Changes in Climate

If you are lucky enough to escape the icy winds and snows in winter with a trip to the tropics, or relieve the heat and humidity of the summer with a vacation to ski country, remember it takes your skin a while to adjust. Cell turnover and sebum production speed up gradually in summer, slow down gradually in winter—so take extra precautions when you change climates suddenly.

WHEN YOU GO FROM COLD TO WARM WEATHER:

■ Be extra careful about the sun. In the tropics, sun is more dangerous than at home. You're closer to the equator, so the sun is nearer. Also, it's probably been several months since your last exposure to sun.
■ Use a good sunscreen and limit first-day exposure to forty-five minutes or an hour, but not all at one time.
■ Moisturize all over and frequently. Add oil to your bath.

WHEN YOU GO FROM WARM TO COLD WEATHER:

■ Protect your skin with moisturizer, lip gloss, hand cream. Use a sunscreen if you go out in the snow.
■ Protect your eyes with eye cream, and goggles or dark glasses. Have a warm bath when you get home, with plenty of bath oil. Apply body cream liberally.

Remember, good skin is healthy skin, and forms the basis for the spectacular makeup effects described in the next few pages.

The magic of M

*P*lay with makeup

Makeup can create magic effects, either subtle or dramatic.
If you practice the art, you can learn how to bring your own
best features to the fore, to make your face come alive without
ever looking "made up."
    Start by carefully studying the color and texture of your skin
in natural daylight. Is the underlying tone of your skin basically
yellow or red? Is the texture fine or coarse? Feel the underlying
bone structure with your fingers.

Sit before the mirror in natural daylight if at all possible, so
that you get the truest picture of the state of your skin, hair,
and color. If the evening is your special Beauty Time, be sure
you have a good quantity of white light to help you in your
self-assessment. Don't use fluorescent lighting, because it tends
to dull and wash out red tones and emphasize blues.
    Now you are ready to make a list of your makeup goals.
Decide which are your best features and how you can learn to
play them up. You don't want to concentrate on eye makeup to
the exclusion of everything else—that sort of unbalanced face
is completely outdated—but you will want to practice all the
little enhancements for pretty eyes, as well as discover which
lipstick colors can create a well-shaped, sensuous mouth; how
to use different colors for a glowing blush; how to choose a
foundation to enhance your skin.
    Talking about makeup can make it seem complicated. It's
not. You'll be surprised at how quick and easy these methods
and tips really are. If it looks time consuming, that's because
every little step is explained in the directions. That's to make
it easy to do, whether you're skilled or taking your first flyer
with makeup. It's the opposite of those recipes sometimes

passed along by very experienced cooks that say "Bake until it's done"—which sounds simple until you realize that you have no idea how high the oven temperature should be, or how it looks when it is done.

THE STEPS TO A PERFECT, FINISHED MAKEUP

Every woman works out her own favorite pattern of doing things, but you might enjoy reviewing your sequence of applying makeup and checking it against the one most professional makeup artists advise:
1. Brow shaping and maintenance (usually the night before so skin recovers from any irritation).
2. Cleansing, toning, and moisturizing.
3. Concealer (optional).
4. Foundation.
5. Contour and shading (optional, usually for evening).
6. Powder—depending on the form of eye and cheek colors you use.
7. Blusher.
8. Eye shadow.
9. Eyeliner.
10. Eyelash curling.
11. Mascara.
12. Brow coloring, if necessary.
13. Powder—if not used before.
14. Lipstick and gloss.

THE NATURAL BROW

Your eyebrows define the mood of your entire face and provide a mobile frame for your eyes. Let the drama come from your eyes—keep eyebrows natural, in proportion to the size of your eyes, and neat. Pencil-thin brows à la Dietrich or aggressive brows like Joan Crawford's belong on The Late Show, not on your 1980s face.

The natural brow is not only the most flattering for your face, it's also the easiest to have. These sketches show you how to use a pencil and a mirror to find where your eyebrows should begin, arch, and end.

Tweezing should be done at night to allow any redness or irritation of the skin to subside before you apply makeup in the morning. Saturate a cotton ball with alcohol or skin toner and use it to remove any trace of oil from brows and fingers.

Cleanse tweezers with alcohol. Hold skin taut between thumb and forefinger. Pluck in the direction of hair growth, one hair at a time. Remove any unwanted hair from below the brow and between the brows, but do not tweeze from the upper curve of the brow. Finish by wiping the brow with a cotton pad dampened with skin toner.

Most brows need little or no darkening. If you use a pencil, go slowly, and stop to check as you go along. The eyebrow should be made up of delicate, feathery strokes like little individual hairs, not one hard, sharp pencil line.

You may find that you need only brush your eyebrows for a finished and balanced look. There are specially designed brushes that are ideal for brushing brows upward, then out into a smooth, natural arch.

UNDERCOVER WORK

A creamy concealer stick can be a fabulous tool for lightening circles under eyes or camouflaging dark marks on the skin. There are some basic tricks to using it, though. Here they are: **DO** use concealer stick after moisturizing and before foundation. **DON'T** go too light. Choose a concealer shade that is a half shade lighter than your own skin tone. **DO** apply concealer *just below,* rather than directly on, dark under-eye circles, and blend up into the dark area. Dot on, starting at the corner of the eye and continuing toward the hairline. Then blend. **DON'T** try to lighten the area drastically. Slight shadowing under the eye looks more natural. **DON'T** use a concealer if the problem is puffiness. A light concealing stick will cause bags to come forward visually and so look worse. A temporary wrinkle smoother will minimize the bags. Sleeping with your head slightly raised helps prevent under-eye puffiness. And remember, fresh cucumber slices or cotton balls soaked with witch hazel really work wonders on puffy eyes. **DO** dot concealer directly on blemishes and blend with fingertips.

Three women—one in her twenties, one in her thirties, one in her forties...
Your own technique makes makeup work wonders. Here, three women follow three very individual makeup plans best suited to their age, skin and bone structure.

In her twenties (top), this woman dots blemishes with concealer to blend with a fingertip. In her thirties (center), this woman blends out patches of uneven color with a concealer stick. In her forties (bottom), this woman uses concealer just below (not on) dark under-eye circles.

FOUNDATION:

GRAND ILLUSION

The beautiful illusion of flawless skin is what foundation offers. Properly chosen and applied, foundation smooths and evens the tone and texture of the skin, causing little imperfections to become less apparent.

You might not choose to wear foundation every day, and if your skin is very good, you might not choose to wear foundation all over. But the right foundation is an indispensable aid to a really beautiful, subtle makeup.

There are two basic kinds of foundation: Liquid and Cream. Each is available in three formulations:

<u>Oil-based</u>—the color is suspended in oil. Can look heavy if you are not skilled in application.

<u>Water-based</u>—a tiny amount of oil emulsified with lots of water suspends the color. Looks natural and helps moisturize the skin. Excellent for normal to dry skin.

<u>Oil-Free</u>—the color suspension contains no oils and may even absorb oil from the skin. Best for oily skin.

There are three finishes:

<u>Dewy</u>—moist, glowing look—helps minimize tiny lines.

<u>Matte</u>—smooth, even, no-shine look for normal or oily skin.

<u>Semi-matte</u>—smooth, even effect for all skin types. Use sheer for near-perfect complexion, medium to conceal flaws, and heavy to alter skin tone.

Shade: The right shade will blend to invisibility on your skin. Match your skin tone as closely as possible, by choosing color in natural daylight; try it on your face, along the jaw or on the forehead. If you can't see where it begins and ends —it is the right shade.

THE BEST WAY TO APPLY FOUNDATION

Apply foundation after cleansing, toning, moisturizing and, if it's part of your makeup plan, after using concealer.

Apply lightly and sparingly with a clean fingertip across cheeks, along nose, across forehead, across eyelids, and along chin.

Blend up and out over the skin wherever foundation is needed to smooth and even out skin tone. If you have good skin, you needn't cover your face entirely. Do cover tiny discolorations, broken capillaries, veins in the eyelids, and shiny patches. If you use foundation over areas where there is downy fuzz, such as the upper lip, use it sparingly because foundation will accentuate the hair.

Be careful to avoid getting foundation into the hairline, as the effect is very unattractive. To help prevent this, use a ribbon or towel to hold your hair off your face.

Feather out the foundation with smooth upward and outward strokes. Then blend down along the jawbone and feather out along the underside of the jawbone. There should be no line of demarcation where the foundation stops. (That's why choosing the shade closest to your natural skin tone is so important.) Blending makeup down the neck leads to unsightly collar rings.

For oily skin (top), oil-free foundation is the answer. Normal-to-dry skin (center), gets smooth-flowing color with a moisturizing foundation. Mature skin (bottom), which tends to be drier, welcomes a soft, dewy finish and medium coverage to minimize tiny lines.

1. Start with the smallest amount you think possible.
2. Use your lightest touch when blending around eye area, where surplus makeup tends to cake.
3. Very good skins and very dark skins always look best with a very sheer foundation.

SPECIAL EFFECTS: SHADE AND CONTOUR

In the movie business, an Academy Award is given for Special Effects. Makeup artists deserve some kind of award for the special effects they achieve using powders and creams to shade and contour a face. A clever makeup artist can create a slim, symmetrical face with perfect features no matter what the bare face looks like. The major principle to keep in mind is that light reveals, dark conceals. To bring out a feature, use a light color on it. To minimize it, a dark one.

These are the Basic Shading Corrections.

Full cheeks: Draw a triangle with one long side following the lower edge of the cheekbone, a short side near the hairline down to the earlobe and the third side to a point just under the center of your eye.

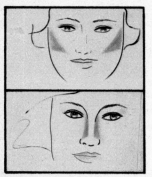

Wide nose: Draw a narrow triangle on each side of your nose from bridge to nostril. Feather out toward cheeks.

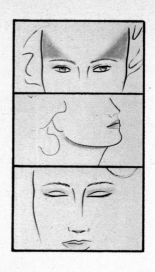

Broad forehead: Shade in a triangle over the brow into the temple.

Slack jawline: Lift your head, and shade just under the jawbone.

Long nose: Shade under the tip of the nose.

USING POWDER
LIKE A PROFESSIONAL

Now or later, be sure to take advantage of powder's benefits. It sets your makeup to help it look better longer, and does away with shine.

TIPS ON USING POWDER

■ Deep-toned skins can look gray if powder is too light. Look for translucent powder in deep shades.

■ Use translucent powder to look less tired at the end of a long day. Pat lightly along the outside of your face—across your forehead at the hairline, all along the jawline and chin, and on the tip of your nose. It gives a soft, flattering halo of light.

■ Use loose powder to help blend powder blush. Dip a soft powder brush into loose face powder. Blow off the excess; then dip the brush into your powder blush, and brush on with quick strokes. The blush blends into your makeup instantly, with no line of demarcation.

GETTING A GLOW ON

Who can do without blusher? It makes everybody look better: glowing, healthy, and alive.

Tip: Stick to the same color family for cheek color and lip color. Use rose with rose and peach with peach.

Tip: Blush that looks too dark in the bottle or compact may be the perfect choice. Blush is concentrated pigment. One that appears too deep will blend out to a glow on your skin. But blush color that's too light just sits there on your skin looking artificial.

PICK THE BLUSH YOU PREFER

■ Powder blush produces a soft, matte finish—a great choice for normal-to-oily skin. Use it over your foundation and powder. Do use a good, fluffy brush.

■ Cream blush (stick or compact) blends to a sheer, natural glow. It glides on over foundation before you powder. Ideal for normal to dry skins.

■ Liquid or gel blush puts a wash of transparent color over foundation makeup and under face powder. For all but the driest skin types.

Special Tip: Frosted blush adds a pearlescent shimmer to your skin. It is available in all forms of blush. Use it to put shimmery color on over your foundation, then blend to a soft luster. Finish with face powder. Great for evening!

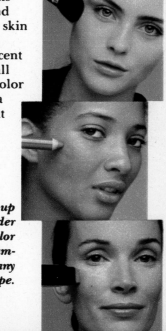

Radiant color! How to glow is up to you. (Top) Fluff-on powder blush. (Center) Versatile color pencils. (Bottom) Handy cream-stick blush. All are great for any skin type.

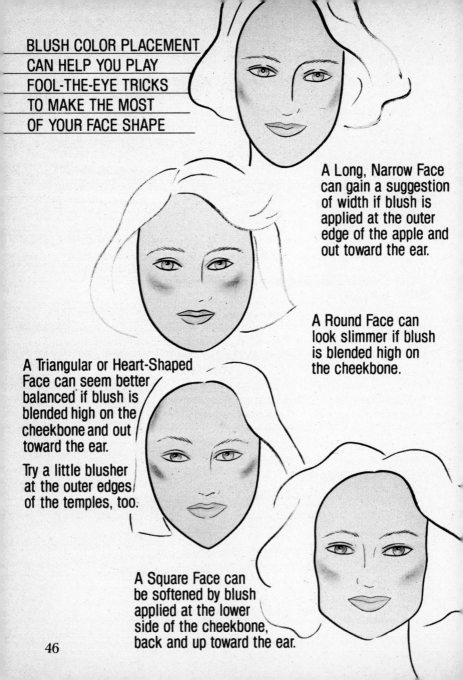

BLUSH COLOR PLACEMENT
CAN HELP YOU PLAY
FOOL-THE-EYE TRICKS
TO MAKE THE MOST
OF YOUR FACE SHAPE

A Long, Narrow Face
can gain a suggestion
of width if blush is
applied at the outer
edge of the apple and
out toward the ear.

A Round Face can
look slimmer if blush
is blended high on
the cheekbone.

A Triangular or Heart-Shaped
Face can seem better
balanced if blush is
blended high on the
cheekbone and out
toward the ear.

Try a little blusher
at the outer edges
of the temples, too.

A Square Face can
be softened by blush
applied at the lower
side of the cheekbone,
back and up toward the ear.

46

WHERE DOES BLUSH GO?

That's the most frequently asked question in Avon's beauty seminars around the country. The answer is easy: Put blush color right where you blush naturally, in the middle of your cheekbones—the so-called "apple" of your cheek.

VERY IMPORTANT TIPS

■ Don't bring color up or in too close to the eyes from below. This makes them look smaller and puffier.
■ Don't bring color in too close to the nose. This closes up the face.
■ Never bring color down too far on your face. This makes you look drawn. Stop at a point even with the bottom of your nostrils, or even above.

4 POINTERS ON BLUSH

1. The deeper your skin tone, the brighter your blush can be.
2. Good bones deserve to be accentuated by brighter blush. If your cheekbones are high and chiseled, go bright.
3. Party lights—all artificial lights—call for more vibrant blush color.
4. For a high-key evening makeup, top off makeup with a quick, light stroke of frosted stick blush just over the tops of your cheekbones for a shimmering accent.

Where to blush? Depends on you: Soften angularity (top), with blush high on cheekbone and out toward your ear. To slim a round face (center), blush high on cheekbone. Widen a narrow face (bottom), with blush at outer edge of the apple; blend out toward the ear.

EYES

The beautiful first impression you create depends on your beautiful eyes—often the first thing about you others notice. But what they see when looking into your eyes is up to you. With today's makeup and a little practice you can have eloquent expressive eyes.

EYE SHADOW: FOR LIVELY, ELOQUENT EYES

It all starts with eye shadow—it's shape and color, richness and drama, easy enhancement and fun to play with.

Revel in the fiesta of color for eyes. Use at least two tones—a medium or deep color to shade, a lighter tone to highlight: just one color at a time looks old-fashioned.

Using a blue eyeshadow to match blue eyes is another outdated makeup approach. Today we have learned that a complementary color—a reddish brown, for example—will intensify blue eyes by contrast, while a blue shadow will just overpower blue eyes.

Here is a list of just a few of the interesting results you can bring about through using complementary colors for shadows.

EYE SHADOW CHART

Eye Color	Shadow	Effect
BLUE	Brown	intensifies blue
	Beige	deepens or brings out gray
	Pink	makes blue seem bright, clear
	Plum	deepens, accentuates
GREEN or HAZEL	Charcoal	makes eyes seem greener
	Brown	brings out gold or brown
	Deep blue	makes green clearer
	Pink	brightens the effect of green
BROWN	Blue-gray	all tend to enrich the
	Sage	depth and warmth of
	Green	brown eyes through
	Plum	contrast
	Lilac	
BLACK	Plum	all tend to draw attention
	Copper	to the eye and to enliven
	Vivid pink	the eye area
	Deep turquoise	

DEPENDING ON THE COLORS YOU USE

to shadow and highlight, and where you place them, you can change the whole dimension of the eye area. Here, in sketches, the game plan. Look it over, then pick the shadow plays that do the most for your eyes.

1. TO MAKE EYES LOOK LARGER

Sweep color out to the side, along eye bone, under lower lid.

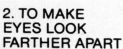

3. TO MAKE EYES LOOK DEEPER SET

Put lots of color in the crease. Avoid pale, frosted shades.

2. TO MAKE EYES LOOK FARTHER APART

Sweep color up and out from center to outer corners of lid.

4. TO MAKE EYES LOOK MORE OPEN

Shadow all along the lid, lots of color in the crease.

50

5. TO MAKE EYES LOOK MORE PROMINENT

*Concentrate color
on the eye bone;
use a light or frosted
shade on the lid.*

7. TO MAKE EYES LOOK LESS DROOPING

*Carry color slightly upward at outer
corner of the eye. A second shadow
color in a lighter, harmonizing shade
can be very effective on **the eye bone**
at the outer corner.*

6. TO MAKE EYES LOOK LESS ROUND

*Shadow the lid only,
shading up and out
at the outer corner.*

*Sweep the color out to
the side along the eye
bone (top), to make eyes
look larger. Use more
color on the eye bone
and put light or frosted
shade on the lid (center),
to make eyes look more
prominent. Sweep color
up and out to the side
(bottom), to make eyes
seem farther apart.*

GOOD CLEAN LINES

Eye liner is back, and it's nothing like the patent-leather look of the past. Using liquids or pencils, it's possible to draw on the finest, most controlled line if you rest your elbow on a table to steady your hand for maximum balance and control.

Look straight into a mirror with your eyes half closed, lids relaxed. You might want to place the tip of your ring finger at the outer corner of your eye and press gently, slightly toward the temple, to hold the eyelid taut.

Draw the thinnest line you can, moving from the center of the lid to the outer corner. Stay as close as possible to the roots of the lashes. Now draw from the inner corner to the center of the upper lid. Lining in two steps this way is easier than drawing one continuous line.

1. Draw the line just from the center out on the upper lid, and just at the very outer corner of the lower lid, not beyond, to make eyes look wider than ever.

2. Line upper lid all the way across. Then line the lower lid from the outer corner to about halfway in for an extra-intense evening gaze.

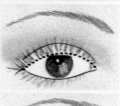

3. Dot—don't line—just between lash roots along the upper lid. This takes a little practice, but gives lots of definition and sparkle.

4. Rim the eye with color by lining the inner lids, top and bottom, with a soft pencil. Blue makes the white of the eye look whiter; black makes the eye look very dramatic.

UPSWEPT LASHES TO OPEN YOUR EYES

Curling lashes before applying mascara opens up the eye. When the white of the eye isn't shadowed by overhanging lashes, it looks clearer, whiter, and brighter. A row of upswept lashes helps disguise prominent or puffy eyelids, too. If you wear glasses, curling is a must to keep lashes from sweeping the lenses. Crimp lashes with the eyelash curler, squeezing gently as you slowly count to ten. That's it!

DENSE, DARK LASHES

Help yourself to wonderful lashes with mascara. Even when you decide to do without any other eye makeup, do curl your lashes and sweep on a little mascara to darken them. Mascara is the one form of eye makeup that looks good at any age. Automatic mascara with its bristly little wand brush is the easiest to use. Here's the best way to apply mascara. Do the top side of your upper lashes first. Tilt your head forward, with your eyes half closed. Slowly sweep mascara from base to tips on the top side of the upper lashes. For the underside of your upper lashes, tilt your head back, eyes open wide. To apply mascara to your lower lashes, tilt your head forward and use the tip of the wand.

For extra lushness, let your mascara dry for a minute. Then dust a little face powder over your lashes and apply a second coat of mascara. You'll love the extra length and fullness.

TIPS FOR LASHES

■ Clumping of lashes is caused by rushing mascara application. Go slowly, and separate lashes with a brush if necessary. Using the tip of the wand eliminates clumping.
■ The sun bleaches lashes at the tips in no time. Keep lashes covered with mascara. Try waterproof mascara at the beach. It works.
■ Evening makeup trick: Use two coats of black or black/ brown mascara. Then tip the lashes with emerald green or sapphire blue.

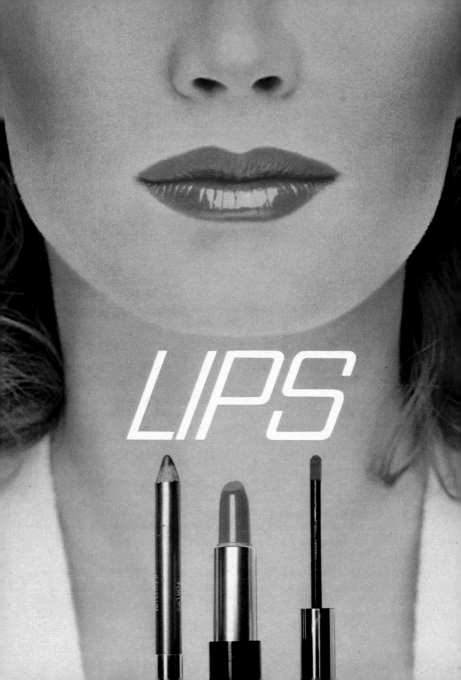

To many people, lipstick **is** makeup. Lipstick is the first thing a child grabs when she plays grown-up. In wartime, lipstick was the one cosmetic governments deemed essential to morale.

COLOR FOR A BEAUTIFUL MOUTH

1. **Shape** the outline. You want a clean, smooth edge, not a blurry one. The way to achieve this is by outlining. An outline will also prevent the fill-in lip color you use from "feathering" up into tiny lines along your upper lip. To shape the outline, use a lip brush or freshly sharpened lip-liner pencil. If you use a brush, keep the pinky of your hand resting on the tip of your chin for accuracy and control.

Outline the upper lip first, one side at a time. Start in the center of the lip and draw out to the corner in one continuous sweep for the cleanest line. On the lower lip, draw from corner to corner.

2. **Color** your lips. Apply the fill-in color so that it blends invisibly into the outline.

3. **Shine** your lips with gloss, clear or tinted, for attention-getting gleam. For a softer glow, omit the finishing gloss. But never blot your lipstick. That not only dulls your lipstick, it robs the lips of color.

Outline a beautiful mouth:

Top—If lips are shapely, follow the natural line.

Center—If too generous, stay just inside the lip line to slim.

Bottom—If too thin, color just over lipline for more voluptuous lips.

USE COLOR TO CORRECT THE SHAPE OF YOUR LIPS

1. **For thin lips,** draw just over the natural line and fill in with a light or bright color. Finish with gloss.

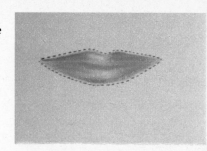

2. **For wide lips,** stop the outline just short of the natural corners. Fill in the center of the lips with a shade that is slightly darker than the one you use in the corners.

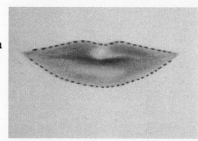

3. **For full lips,** outline just inside the natural line and stop just shy of the corners. Fill in with a medium or dark color and omit lip gloss.

4. **To make pouty lips,** use a darker color to fill in the lower lip, a lighter one on the upper lip. Reverse if you want to bring out a timid lower lip. Keep the difference in the shades subtle—just a little lighter and darker—or this trick is too obvious. Omit lip gloss on the lower lip if a pout is the problem. But use gloss if you want to bring out the lower lip.

TIPS FOR LIPS

1. Make your lips more seductive by blending a tiny dot of clear lip gloss to highlight; place it just at the natural bow of your upper lip.

2. When you want a very delicate, natural look, try this: Outline with a very soft, pale shade of lip pencil. Blend well into the lips using a lipstick brush, but don't add fill-in color. Instead, use a little clear gloss over your lips.

3. Unless your teeth are very white and very even, you will find that soft lip colors or rich, muted ones are more flattering than vivid bright ones. Orangey shades make teeth look yellow.

4. To make your mouth look very soft and sensual, try using lip gloss just in the center of the mouth on both upper and lower lips.

5. For evening, use a deeper tint of lip gloss to finish your lips. You can also make the shape more seductive by finishing off the usual procedure with another touch of the lip-liner pencil. Use it just in the curve of the bow on your upper lip and at the center point below your lower lip; blend it into the gloss.

Color and shine complete the perfect mouth. You can fill in color after outlining color—with a lip pencil, lipstick (top), or a lip brush (center). Final pretty touch for every pair of lips, the slick of gloss (bottom).

Upbea —that' world wr results lik spending.

58

t good looks, the spark and clean-cut prettiness you see here
what it's all about. Making up makes you ready to face the
th all your natural good looks front and center....End
this are why makeup practice time is well worth
These three makeup plans went from naked skin to

WOW

perfection in well under 15 minutes. Once your own routine is honed and habitual, it becomes child's play to do a perfect makeup in minutes, freeing you to get on with your life looking and feeling this assured, this polished, this ready for hours and hours of good times without further thought about good looks.

Glorious hair

When a woman's hair looks good, she feels happy about herself, energetic, and pretty no matter what she is wearing. During your Beauty Time one week, concentrate on your hair. Perhaps this will be the beginning of a new, beautiful you.

After a shower, bath, or shampoo, use your fingers to comb your hair off your face while it is still damp. Then let it dry naturally, brush it, and study yourself carefully with two mirrors to observe all the angles. Using your fingers, comb your hair in different ways—push it forward into bangs, hold it up, sweep it back. This is the first step in helping you decide what kind of a haircut is best for you. But of course it is only a professional who can predict how a cut, a style, will work for you.

It often helps, though, if you can show the stylist what you have in mind, since most of us are at a loss for words in describing a hair style. Before your appointment, go through recent issues of your favorite women's magazines to find a few photos of hair styles that you like and think will look good on you.

Cut them out, and when you go in to see the stylist for a cut, take them along. Don't be shy about expressing what you want. A good stylist welcomes every clue to what will make the client look better, because then she will be a better walking ad for the salon.

SOME CONSIDERATIONS
ABOUT CUT AND STYLE

■ A blunt cut is always healthier for hair, because it leaves only a small area of the ends of the hair exposed to moisture loss and splitting.

■ Minimal layering may be necessary to control curly hair.

■ Split ends can be eliminated only by cutting them off—perhaps as much as two inches.

■ A mature face may be flattered by shorter hair, but not by tight short hair. Softness around the face is much more becoming to an older woman than severity. Gray or white hair usually looks best if there is a bit of movement or wave away from the face, and looks less good when worn tight against the head.

■ A thick neck or a double chin is greatly helped by slightly longer hair curving in just under the jawline.

Study yourself.... Using your fingers, comb your hair around in different ways. How does it look swept back, or forward in bangs?

BRUSH FOR LUBRICATION

The purpose of brushing is to lubricate the hair. Your brush should relate to your hair's texture and length—soft bristles for fine hair, stronger bristles for coarse, curly hair. Natural bristles are good because they are gentle and absorb oil and dirt.

Twenty strokes are more than enough to clean and shine hair, dislodge loose hairs, and whisk away surface dirt and hairspray buildup. Be sure to brush nightly if your hair is dry. Everyone should brush before a shampoo to get oil up and off the scalp for the most thorough cleaning. But never brush wet hair or even damp hair. Hair is very elastic when wet and brushing can stretch it to the breaking point. Use a wide-toothed comb instead. The best combs are flexible with blunt, rounded teeth.

BEAUTY BASICS FOR HAIR

Of all the things you can do to make your hair look better, there's only one you *must* do: *Shampoo.*

Wash as often as you like— at least once a week, even every day if you wish (but naturally, with a milder shampoo). Don't worry about over-drying hair: If you use only a small amount of the correct shampoo (one formulated for dry, oily, or normal hair) and lather only once, your hair will not dry out.

Chemists measure the state of the hair like the skin, on the pH scale, from 0 to 14. Healthy hair has a pH reading of 4.0 to 5.0, which is slightly acid. When hair is immersed in an alkaline solution—like soap and water—the hair swells and the cuticle lifts to the utmost. The dirt and oils on the hair are washed off but the hair itself is coated with a film of alkaline residue, which keeps the cuticle lifted and the hair looking dull. An acid cleanser, on the other hand, inhibits lathering and does not cause the hair cuticle to swell enough to allow for real cleansing. The solution is to use a mild, gentle shampoo that is pH-balanced and will leave your hair in a neutral state (pH 7). In order to restore it to pH 4 to 5, use an instant conditioning rinse immediately after shampooing. It will coat the hair shaft to make hair softer and shinier. In a pinch, an old-fashioned lemon or vinegar rinse can be used to restore normal pH: add a tablespoon of lemon juice or vinegar to a pint of water for the next-to-last rinse. But avoid these homemade rinses if you have had a permanent or your hair has been colored; they can be very drying.

HOW TO SHAMPOO

1. Brush your hair to distribute oil and loosen dead cells from the scalp.
2. Use warm water. Wet hair thoroughly. Throw your head back so the soil rinses out of your hair and runs off behind you, not down your face.
3. Pour a small amount of shampoo into your wet palm. Rub your palms together to work up lather, then comb through your hair with your fingers. Work suds from your scalp to the ends and gently massage.
4. Rinse thoroughly in warm water.
5. Do not lather again unless your hair is very dirty or oily, but do rinse again and again.
6. Use an instant conditioner or cream rinse right after rinsing shampoo out of your hair to give hair added shine and body.
7. Gently towel dry.

PUT HAIR IN PEAK CONDITION

There are also conditioners designed for helping repair hair that's been damaged by the weather or by chemical processes. These intensive-conditioning treatments are sometimes used with heat to obtain really penetrating results within a ten- to thirty-minute period. If your hair isn't as supple and lustrous as you like, investigate intensive-conditioning treatment products.

HEAT AND HAIR

Excessive heat is not good for hair, so keep your blow dryer on the Cool or Low setting as much as possible and keep it moving around. Hold it at least 6 inches from your hair.

Many hairdressers now agree that you shouldn't blow-dry every day if you can help it.

TIPS ON GETTING PROFESSIONAL RESULTS WITH THE BLOW DRYER

■ Your hair should be damp-dry before you begin.

■ Start drying at a higher setting, then switch to a lower one when the hair is still somewhat damp.

■ Always hold the dryer at least 6 inches away from the hair and keep it in motion.

■ Styling as you dry is possible with a round (bottle) brush with heat-resistant nylon bristles. You need a larger brush if your hair is long or thick, a smaller one for short hair. Be sure your hair is almost dry before you start using the brush. Styling with the brush gives hair a much softer and more natural look than it could have if you had put it in rollers and then dried it.

■ Section your hair before you begin to dry it. Use a wide-toothed comb and part the hair into the following sections: sides, sides front, sides back, back, and top front. Dry one section at a time—sides first and top front last.

■ For more volume, part the hair into small sections and use the dryer and styling brush against the natural growth pattern.

■ For fullness, hang your head forward so that your hair hangs upside down while you use the dryer.

■ For smooth hair, direct the air current from the dryer down from above and brush the hair downward with long, smooth strokes.

■ For straighter hair, use the brush to grab the ends of your hair; then twist the brush downward so the hair is held taut. Direct air across the top of the hair. Work slowly all around the head, section by section.

■ To turn your hair under, use the brush to twirl the hair from underneath. Roll the brush down and under. Aim the dryer under the brush.

■ For a flip-up, twist the hair around the brush from above, sliding the brush down and rolling it upward at the end. Aim the air flow up from under, and over the hair on the brush.

Note: Many of today's shorter styles look best when you use a dryer that does not blow the hair. A heat lamp might be ideal for your look.

TO STRAIGHTEN HAIR, WAVE IT, OR CURL IT

A permanent can curl hair into ringlets or merely add waves and fullness. It shapes the hair into an S that's tight for curls, loose for waves. Hair is wound around perm rods (small rods for tight curls, big ones for waves) and a lotion is applied that releases chemical bonds, which hold the hair in its natural shape. The lotion is left on the hair for an exact period of time — follow the package directions carefully. Then a neutralizing solution is applied to the hair to lock the new shape into the hair. This solution is then washed out, and the permanent is complete.

Your hair should be in peak condition before a permanent. You might need one or two conditioning treatments beforehand. After the perm, wait at least three full weeks before coloring your hair. Always use shampoos and conditioners made for dry or processed hair after having a permanent.

Hair straightening is a process similar to a permanent. A lotion or cream is applied to break down and soften the hair shaft, then rinsed out; a neutralizer fixes the straightened shape.

Before straightening, and after, plenty of conditioning is advisable. Straightened hair should be treated very gently.

Don't attempt to combine straightening with coloring. It can be disastrous. One model, who both streaked and straightened her hair, got up one morning and found that all her streaks had stayed in bed. The straightened, streaked hair had fallen out and was lying all over her pillow! It is best to treat hair gently, experimenting with one process at a time. A little care now can save you a great deal of care later.

One great cut to wear several ways is the big idea in hair now. Short cuts are easy to work with, and to change for different looks.

The short curly cut looks great in its natural state (big picture), pulled back off the face (below left), or slicked back and jeweled with a flower or a barrette.

Long hair invites playing with —it can be worn up, down, any way you choose. Even with versatile long hair, though, a great cut (to shape, to snip off dead-looking ends) and good care and conditioning make hair easier to work with and prettier.

The magic of color!

Sooner or later you may decide it's not enough to have clean, healthy, well-cut hair. You want hair with some magic. You want color.

Subtle is the big word in hair color. The most flattering new color is one no more than one or two shades away from your own natural hair color. This slight shift of color emphasis can be enough to give you a vibrant new image, without necessitating frequent touchups.

Top professional colorists use colors—plural—not just a single color for an entire head of hair. Another tactic of the professional is to color hair selectively—a few strands here and there to frame the face, or add highlights. And coloring may help your hair's condition. Every color product now has built-in conditioners that may make hair look shinier, feel thicker, and be more manageable. Permanent hair coloring products give hair more body.

TIPS ON HAIR COLOR

When choosing a color, remember:

■ Pigment in hair and skin are closely related and both become less vivid in coloring as we age. That's why it's a mistake to try to duplicate the color your hair was at sixteen when you color it twenty years later. Brunettes will find a lighter shade more flattering; blonds will probably find a less-bright shade more becoming.

■ Avoid unnatural contrasts between skin and hair.

■ Redheads and dark brunettes should be wary of going blond. Touchups will be needed very frequently. Stay with a lighter shade of your natural color and add blond highlights for best results.

■ Streaking, frosting, highlighting, and tipping all involve minimal maintenance, usually a touchup two to four times a year.

BEAUTY RITUAL

your great escape

*M*ake your bath your private spa

From the days of Cleopatra, the bath has been the classic setting for beauty rituals. Set aside an hour or two during which you have nothing on your mind but doing good things for yourself, small attentions that will make you look and feel prettier all week.

Even if you are a confirmed shower person, you owe yourself the weekly treat of at least one deliciously relaxing beauty bath. Here's the suggested procedure for making the most of the bath and the beauty ritual as part of the bath experience.

1. Assemble everything you'll need for a manicure and pedicure (see pages 78, 80). Remove old nail enamel and shape your nails with an emery board.

2. If you use a chemical depilatory or an electric razor to remove hair from legs and under arms, do this now before entering the bath. Rinse off all vestige of the cream before entering the bath.

3. Follow your usual plan for cleansing your face. You might want to apply a cleansing or moisturizing facial mask.

4. After you have shampooed your hair, use a conditioner. If you use an instant conditioner, rinse and gently towel dry. If you use an intensive conditioner, leave on your hair as per package directions. In either case, make a towel turban for your hair.

5. Draw the bath. The water should be warm but not hot.

6. Lie back and soak for about ten minutes, letting your mind go blank.

7. Rub a pumice stone on the rough areas of the body: the bottoms of your feet and your elbows. Push back the cuticles of your nails. Scrub your fingernails and toenails with a nail brush.

8. Use a magnifying mirror and slant-edge tweezers to clean away any straggly growth around your eyebrows.

9. While you let the water out of the tub and run fresh warm water in, use a bath brush, a back brush, a loofah sponge, or other favorite means of scrubbing up a glowing skin all over your body.

10. If you have applied a facial mask, remove it now as the manufacturer directs; then splash your face with clear running water.

11. If you used an intensive conditioning treatment on your hair, remove towel turban, turn on the shower while the tub is draining and rinse out the conditioner.

12. If you use a safety razor to remove body hair, now is the time to soap your legs and underarms and shave them. The warm bath has a softening effect on hair and makes shaving easier.

13. Step out of the tub and wrap yourself in a big, fresh towel to pat yourself dry. Smooth on body moisturizer.

14. Now begin your pedicure.

15. Dry and style your hair.

16. If you are staying home, manicure after doing your hair; if you're going out, apply makeup and fragrance before your manicure.

"The bath is a classic setting for beauty rituals."

THE PERFECT PEDICURE

1. Remove old nail enamel, as for a manicure. Clip toenails no shorter than the tips of the toes, with edges squared to discourage ingrown nails. File rough edges smooth with an emery board. If nails are heavily ridged, smooth them with the smooth side of the emery board. Smooth cuticle remover around sides and base of the nails, and push cuticle back gently.
2. If you have not already accomplished this in the bath, soak your feet in warm, sudsy water. Scrub toenails and feet with a sudsy nail brush. Use a wet pumice stone to smooth away dead skin, calluses, and rough spots on heels and bottoms of feet, or use a smoothing cream after drying your feet.
3. Dry your feet and gently push back cuticles. Fold tissue and weave it between toes, or use cotton balls to separate toes. Apply base coat to nails on the left foot, then to nails on the right foot. When the base coat dries, apply a thin, even coat of nail enamel to nails of the left foot. Get as close to the cuticle as you can. Now do the right foot. Tidy up any smudges of enamel on skin with a cotton swab dipped in nail-enamel remover. Apply a second coat of enamel; then finish with top coat. When nails are dry, massage cream or lotion into your feet.

A LIST OF PAMPERING TIPS

There's more to the walking-on-air feeling than just a pedicure. Below is a list of some of the things worth doing for your feet.
1. Slip off your shoes to give feet a breather during the day. Make it a real pleasure with refreshing footspray to cool you right through your stockings.
2. Walk barefoot when you can, but only on a springy surface —sand, thick grass, or wall-to-wall carpet. For hard surfaces, give your feet the protection of a resilient sole.
3. Wear heels of varying heights. Wearing the same heel height all the time can cause painful cramping of the calf muscle. And try not to wear the same shoes too many days in a row.
4. Shop for shoes in the early afternoon. Feet swell over the course of the day. Shoes bought late in the afternoon can be too loose next morning; bought in the morning, too tight that night.
5. Massage your feet whenever there's an opportunity.

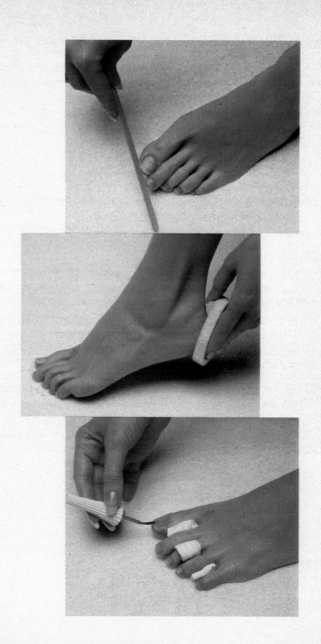

INVEST A LITTLE TIME IN YOUR HANDS

Her manicure—or lack of one—spoiled the effect of Scarlett O'Hara's new dress on Rhett. In real life, too, people notice hands quickly. Hands that are beautifully cared for say you care for yourself and others. And shapely and colorful nails make a statement about your fashion sense.

A weekly manicure is a must for pretty hands. Here is the manicure technique used in expensive salons that you can borrow for home:

Assemble:

Bowl of warm, sudsy water; hand towel; emery board; nail enamel remover; nail clipper; cuticle conditioner; nail strengthener; cuticle remover; cotton pads; orange stick; nail brush; ridge filler (optional); base coat; top coat; nail enamel; nail enamel dryer.

1. Soak cotton pad with nail enamel remover. Press down on nail, using a rocking motion of your thumb on cotton pad to take up all the old enamel; then whisk it off quickly. This gives a cleaner removal than rubbing nail; also, less remover is apt to get into the cuticle.

2. File dry nails with an emery board, toward center of nail in one direction only; don't saw. Shape nails into slightly blunted ovals to discourage splits.

3. Soak fingertips for a minute or two in warm, sudsy water to resoften cuticle and wash away traces of remover. Rinse and dry hands.

4. Smooth cuticle remover into sides and base of each nail. Let it work for a minute or so. Push back cuticles gently, using the orange stick.

5. Dip fingers into warm, sudsy water and brush away old cuticles with sudsy nail brush. Rinse. If you have a hangnail, use the nail clipper to remove the torn skin. Don't clip into the cuticle itself —that encourages more hangnails!

6. Massage cuticle conditioner around the base and sides of each nail. This keeps cuticle strong and pliable to protect nails, and discourages splitting and hangnails. Rinse off excess and dry your hands.

7. Clean, dry nails are now ready for nail strengthener to firm and seal nails against splits, chips, and breaks. Stroke down center first, then sides. Hold brush so it spreads out flat against the nail. A thin, even coat adheres best.

8. Follow with a base coat applied the same way. A base coat helps enamel flow on smoother, cling longer.

9. Apply nail enamel in two thin coats, letting enamel dry between coats. Spread each coat sparingly—one dip of the brush will be enough for one nail. Put down each coat in three smooth strokes from base to tip of nail. Stroke down the center first, then each side.

10. Shield your finished manicure with a thin, even layer of glossy top coat. It adds beautiful gleaming protection so nails look better all week long. Between manicures, you may want to apply fresh top coat every few days. It's a good idea for lasting power and gloss.

11. Apply a product that speeds nail-enamel drying time to help prevent smearing while enamel dries.

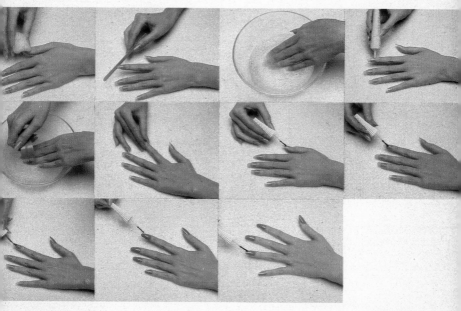

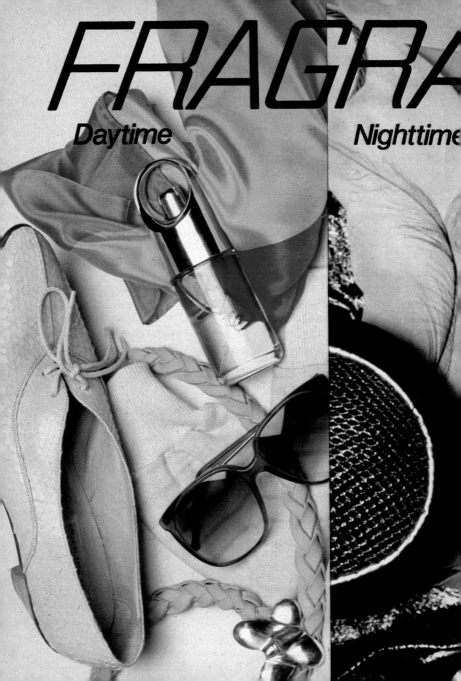

FRAGRA

Daytime

Nighttime

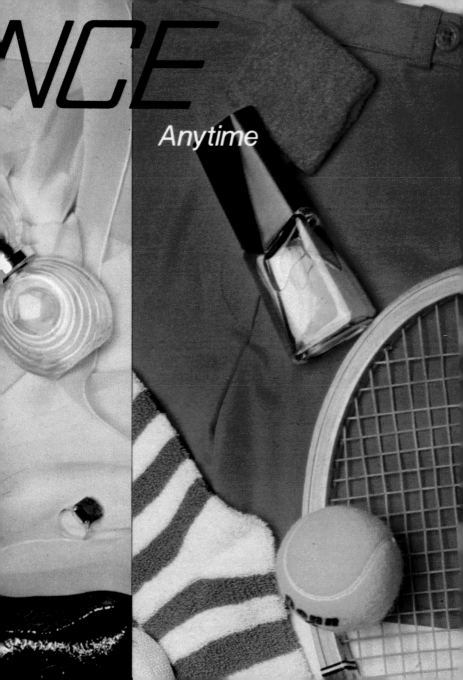

ragrance

Now you're feeling beautiful.

If you have followed the suggestions in this book so far, you will notice a remarkable change in your appearance. Your hair will be softer and shinier; your complexion will look clearer and more radiant; your eyes will be brighter and more sparkling—even your toenails will be shapely and glowing.

And now that you've come this far, we will share with you one of the most important—and most subtle—beauty secrets of them all. We will teach you how to create your own aura and mystique, a memorable impression that softly lingers after you have left the room. The secret is <u>fragrance.</u>

Fragrance in all its delightful variety has always been an important echo of femininity, but today fragrance has become an absolutely essential part of the modern woman's fashion planning. From this day on your fragrance can be thought of as an indispensable addition to your own beauty personality.

At one time perfume was reserved for Special Occasions Only, like wearing a floor-length evening dress, and a woman was given one special "signature fragrance," which she used to commemorate important evenings. But the modern woman thinks all occasions are special and variety the spice of life. Now she buys and wears fragrance every day—and evening—creating her own wardrobe of scent as individual and personal as the clothing she wears.

Although innumerable elements make up the pallette, a perfumer draws upon six basic groups of ingredients:

The Six Great Families of Fragrance

I
Single florals
capture the essence
of a single blossom.

II
Leafy, woodsy,
mossy blends
combine aromatic
woods, such as cedar,
with the aromas of
flower stems, leaves,
ferns, oakmoss and
other herbal scents
for a clean,
refreshing fragrance
with a "foresty"
appeal.

III

Floral bouquets blend a bouquet of different flower notes into an intricate and subtle harmony. It may not be easy to identify the specific flowers combined, but the fragrance is definitely "flowery" in character.

IV

Oriental blends evoke the mystery and richness of the Orient through sophisticated combinations of musk and amber, along with exotic blossoms. These blends are apt to be haunting, intense, and sweet or smoky.

V

Spicy, fruity blends meld the clean, fresh quality of citrus fruits and pungent spices such as clove, cinnamon, or ginger with, perhaps, spicy flower aromas such as carnation, and hints of mellow, peach-like warmth. These are apt to be sparkling, outdoorsy fragrances, light and fresh, but they may shade down into rich, full-bodied fragrances.

VI

Modern Blends may contain notes from any or all other fragrance categories, yet they do not duplicate anything in nature. Rather, these are sparkling new creations of the perfumer. They have a full-bodied total impact that is characterized by a brilliant sparkle.

HOW TO FIND A FRAGRANCE

Although each fragrance cries out "Buy Me!" with its exquisite packaging and exotic name, the way it is advertised can be a real clue to the scent you are searching for. Scents do suggest moods—a "green" fragrance evokes the freshness of the country; musk, a sense of intimacy, romance; lemon, a hint of summer breezes—and manufacturers are quick to name their scents and write their ads in accordance with these psychological associations. An ad that shows a tennis match, for example, tells you that the perfume featured has a light, informal quality, whereas an ad picturing a couple holding hands in the moonlight suggests a more intense, intimate aroma.

But no matter what the ad or your friends say, the only sure way to find a fragrance is to experiment. Get set for an adventure and don't be afraid to take a risk.

When testing a scent, keep in mind that you cannot really tell how a fragrance smells by sniffing it in the bottle. Even when it is on your skin the scent may actually change slightly within the first ten minutes of application.

The immediate perception or first impression of a scent is called the "top note." Moments later the full fragrance will begin to unfold. This stage is referred to as the "middle note" or "heart." The full character or long-term impression of a scent is not discernible until several minutes after application, when it has had time to blend with the natural oils of the skin. The fragrance is altered at this stage by your individual chemistry, which provides the missing note—and makes that fragrance distinctly your own. Perfumers call this stage "drydown." Other people slowly become aware of your fragrance as the warmth of your skin helps the scent radiate outward in the process called diffusion. And of course, as they become aware of your fragrance, they become aware of you, your unique presence, and the very special atmosphere you generate wherever you go.

THE FORMS OF FRAGRANCE

Most women are delighted when they see all the different fragrances on display—lined up in sensually shaped containers, with golden ribbons, pastel colored wrappings, exotic names that evoke faraway places and passionate romance. But how do you choose the right form for you?

Liquids: The most traditional form of fragrance is liquid. Cologne has an alcohol base and comes in varying strengths, depending upon the concentration of perfume oils. The ultra colognes have the greatest strength and are the most long lasting.

Perfume has the highest concentration of perfume oils. It is generally the most expensive and richest form of a fragrance.

Pump Sprays: These are liquid fragrances which are drawn up through a tube and forced out through a small opening in the top. The mist created by the spray covers a wider area of the skin than ordinary splash-on fragrances and results in greater diffusion.

Cream-based: Creams, lotions, and glacé fragrances take slightly longer to diffuse than liquid forms, because the warmth of the skin is necessary to release the fragrance, but they are creamy smooth and luxurious to the touch.

Oil-based: Perfumes are highly concentrated fragrances. They are exceedingly long lasting and very lush and rich in aroma.

SIX BEAUTIFUL WAYS TO CREATE A FRAGRANCE WARDROBE

1. Use your sense of timing. Tests show that the sense of smell grows more acute as the day goes on. Your power is at its peak in the late afternoon. That's the golden hour for testing.
2. Pick your spot. The inside of the wrist (where the pulse beats close to the surface) and the back of the wrist are ideal proving grounds for a drop or a light spray of fragrance.
3. Narrow the field. Try one perfume on the right wrist, one on the left. Don't try to juggle more than two fragrances at a time.

4. Don't rush it. Give perfume and your skin a chance to get acquainted and interact. Remember, it takes several minutes before fragrance develops fully on your skin.

5. Explore your individuality. Each skin's chemistry is unique, so perfume never smells quite the same on any two women. Always sample the way a fragrance smells on *you* before making up your mind about it.

6. Experiment with fragrances. Even when you aren't really in the market for a new one, sample a couple of the new perfumes now and again. Remember, trying out new styles is the way to keep your fashion ideas up-to-date, and the only way to build a flattering wardrobe. You should build your perfume wardrobe in the same manner. Then you can express your personality with fragrance, just as you do with clothes.

FRAGRANCE LAYERING

Once you have chosen a scent, let yourself go—luxuriate in its many forms. Wear them all! This is known in the beauty business as "layering fragrance." For the fullest fragrance impression and the greatest enjoyment, use cologne and perfume together: splash or spray cologne on body, neck, arms, and legs after the bath; then follow with perfume stroked on at the pulse points (temple, back of the ear, base of the throat, over the collarbone, inner elbow, back and inside of the wrist, back of the knee, back of the ankle).

Layering, like so many other beautiful things, might begin in the bath. Use perfumed soap, a matching perfumed bath oil. Follow the bath with a matching fragrance in body lotion and talc, then cologne and perfume. And refresh fragrance periodically (as often as you reapply lipstick is a handy rule of thumb) from a purse spray or other portable form.

Use your favorite scent in all its forms to create a subtle, delicious shimmer of fragrance that wraps you invisibly for hours.

ENJOY FRAGRANCE ALL AROUND YOU

You can extend the pleasures of fragrance to every corner of your life. It can be an enjoyable challenge to your creativity to make the whole house smell wonderful, filled with small surprises of scent.

8 Tips for Surrounding Yourself with Fragrant Delights

1. Tuck sachets among the sheets and towels in the linen closet.
2. Before touching up washable clothes, spray a little cologne on the ironing board. Don't spray fragrance directly on clothes —it may spot.
3. Add a few drops of bath oil to a pot of simmering water, turn off the flame, and let the pot stand. You will add humidity to the atmosphere, which is good for your skin. You also refresh the whole house with fragrance.
4. Save empty perfume and cologne bottles; leave them, caps off, at the bottom of the clothes hamper.

5. Tuck unwrapped perfumed guest soaps in your luggage before storing it. Bags will smell delicious, not musty, next time you pack for a trip.

6. Hang sachets on the coat hangers in your closet. Just two or three will make a whole closetful of clothes smell nice.

7. Some beauty companies provide attractive scented paper as fragrance samples. Save these and tuck them in your lingerie drawer. Or make your own by saturating white blotter paper with your favorite fragrance.

8. To be soothed with lovely smells as you travel, put a pomander in your car.

Of course, these few tips are only a springboard for your imagination. Once you try a couple of them, you will probably find yourself coming up with half a dozen more on your own. Soon, you will become skillful at using just a faint whiff of fragrance to give a little lift to every area of your life. Wherever you go, you will leave behind you, like footprints in the sand, a gentle reminder of a very special you.

A last word on new beginnings

Now, you know a lot about beauty, about being vibrantly healthy. You have the facts and the techniques; but even more important, you now know more about yourself. Just by reading this book you have inevitably been learning about your looks and have begun to get acquainted with yourself in a whole new way. Now is the time to begin to use all this new information to make your own exciting statement, to face the world with the look of the eighties—what we at Avon call "naturalness with style."

Naturalness with style is the flair and vitality of today's woman, a fashion look that is relaxed, current, and fresh. It's the open way you communicate with people, your special enthusiasm for life—all the qualities that make you unique.

You are ready to step forth into the world, radiating that glow and self-confidence that comes from knowing you have never looked so good. But this is only the beginning.

It is difficult to form new beauty habits so thoroughly that they become automatic. And it is easy to slip back into the old, unbeautiful ways. That is why continuous self-assessment is so important. It takes a little time, but will make a big difference. You must promise yourself to:

1. Keep a weekly date with yourself for your Beauty Time. It will take you through the whole week in a well-groomed, confident way.

2. *Keep your new beauty notebook with you at all times and use it. The more often you refer to your record of your goals and your habits, the more clearly you will see the real you—and the easier it will be to make the outer you a more perfect expression of your ideal self.*

3. *Keep going. Don't give up or minimize your dreams, no matter how unattainable they might seem at the start. Your first attempt at a new way of doing eye makeup might be a disappointment. If so, wash that false start away and begin again. You learn a little with every fresh try. Remember, becoming more attractive is an evolving and ongoing process. Experiment and you will keep discovering new ways to improve your appearance. You'll not only look good, but feel beautiful...every day of your life.*

YOU'RE LOOKING GOOD, FEELING BEAUTIFUL

AVON GUARANTEE

If for any reason whatsoever an Avon product is not found satisfactory, it will be cheerfully exchanged or the full purchase price will be immediately refunded upon its return to us or to your Representative.

William P. Chaney
President

Just for you...

AVON BEAUTY COUPONS

Worth $20 in savings on selected Avon products in Campaigns 13, 14 & 15, 1981.
These Beauty Coupons will make shopping the Avon way even more enjoyable!
Redeem them each campaign with your Avon Representative when she
delivers your Order. You'll love the savings—and soon see why
"looking good" was never easier!

Keep this part

AVON BEAUTY COUPON

50¢ OFF

AVON ULTRA COLOGNE
.33 FL. OZ.
IN CAMPAIGN 13, 1981

Ultra Cologne is rich in fragrance oils and emollients that make it ultra long-lasting. Choose from Foxfire, Avon Tasha, Candid, Timeless, Ariane, Tempo, Unspoken, or Emprise.

Keep this part

AVON BEAUTY COUPON

$2 OFF

AVON PROFESSIONAL
MAKEUP BRUSH COLLECTION
IN CAMPAIGN 13, 1981

Be a makeup pro! Set of four natural bristle brushes in an elegant vinyl case help you design beautiful makeup looks.
Contains one Brow/Lash Brush, one Blush Brush, one Lip Brush, and one Eye Shadow Brush. Illustrated instructions included.

Keep this part

AVON BEAUTY COUPON

50¢ OFF

AVON NATURALLY GENTLE
SHAMPOO 8 FL. OZ.
IN CAMPAIGN 13, 1981

So gentle, you can use it everyday for shiny, bouncy, beautiful hair!

Just for you...
AVON BEAUTY COUPONS
Worth $20 in savings
on selected Avon products
in Campaigns 13, 14 & 15, 1981.

Return this part to your Avon Representative

AVON BEAUTY
COUPON
50¢ OFF
AVON ULTRA COLOGNE
.33 FL. OZ.
IN CAMPAIGN 13, 1981

Tear at perforation and give opposite part to your Avon Representative when you order the .33 fl. oz. size of Ultra Cologne in Campaign 13, 1981. Coupon not transferable. Limit: Only one Coupon per purchase.
Special $1.69
With Coupon: $1.19
Lowest Price This Year

Return this part to your Avon Representative

AVON BEAUTY
COUPON
$2 OFF
AVON PROFESSIONAL
MAKEUP BRUSH COLLECTION
IN CAMPAIGN 13, 1981

Tear at perforation and give opposite part to your Avon Representative when you order the Avon Professional Makeup Brush Collection in Campaign 13, 1981. Coupon not transferable. Limit: Only one Coupon per purchase.
Special $10.99
With Coupon: $8.99
Lowest Price Ever

Return this part to your Avon Representative

AVON BEAUTY
COUPON
50¢ OFF
AVON NATURALLY GENTLE
SHAMPOO 8 FL. OZ.
IN CAMPAIGN 13, 1981

Tear at perforation and give opposite part to your Avon Representative when you order the 8 fl. oz. size of Avon Naturally Gentle Shampoo in Campaign 13, 1981. Coupon not transferable. Limit: Only one Coupon per purchase.
Special $1.69
With Coupon: $1.19

Keep this part

AVON BEAUTY
COUPON

$1 OFF

AVON BUBBLE BATH 24 FL. OZ.
IN CAMPAIGN 13, 1981

America's #1 bubble bath makes big, beautiful bubbles even in hard water — and it leaves no bathtub ring.

Keep this part

AVON BEAUTY
COUPON

$1 OFF
EACH

NURTURA REPLENISHING CREAM
(for the face) 2 OZ. NET WT. and
NURTURA REPLENISHING CREAM
FOR THE BODY 5 OZ. NET WT.
IN CAMPAIGN 13, 1981

Moisturizing oils and a sunscreen protect skin from signs of premature aging. Use morning and night for supple, younger-looking skin.

Keep this part

AVON BEAUTY
COUPON

$2 OFF

ANY AVON COUNTRY KITCHEN
COLLECTION PIECE
IN CAMPAIGN 13, 1981

Cheerful kitchen accessories add country charm to any decor. Choose from Magnets and Fragranced Note Pad with Spice Garden Powder Sachet, Ceramic, Salt & Pepper Shakers, Ceramic Trivet, or Moisturized Hand Lotion with Pump Dispenser.

Keep this part

AVON BEAUTY
COUPON

50¢ OFF

AVON SUPER STRENGTHENER
FOR NAILS
IN CAMPAIGN 14, 1981

Helps protect against splitting and breaking. The ideal way to encourage longer, healthier looking nails.

Return this part to your Avon Representative

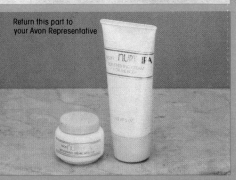

Return this part to your Avon Representative

(Front) Magnets/Fragranced Note Pad/
Sachet **Special $5.99. With Coupon:**
$3.99. (Below) Salt & Pepper Shakers
(set of 2), Ceramic Trivet **Special**
$9.99 each. With Coupon: $7.99 each.
Moisturized Hand Lotion **Special $7.99.**
With Coupon: $5.99.

Return this part to your Avon Representative

Return this part to your Avon Representative

AVON BEAUTY COUPON

$2 OFF

SMOOTH AS SILK BATH OIL
16 FL. OZ.
IN CAMPAIGN 14, 1981

Mixes with water to make every bath a beauty treatment!
Lightly scented. Leaves skin soft and refreshed.

AVON BEAUTY COUPON

$1 OFF EACH

<u>NEW</u> AVON MEN'S TRAVELER
AFTER SHAVE 2 FL. OZ. and
<u>NEW</u> AVON MEN'S TRAVELER
COLOGNE 2 FL. OZ.
IN CAMPAIGN 14, 1981

Convenient size for travel and at-home use. Choice of popular Wild Country, Weekend and Black Suede fragrances.

AVON BEAUTY COUPON

$2 OFF

<u>NEW</u> ROMANTIC RING
IN CAMPAIGN 14, 1981

Looks like an elegant antique ring! Goldtone band centered with a gleaming rhinestone and trimmed with simulated marcasites. Sizes 3, 4, 5, 6, 7, 8, 9.

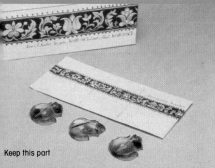

AVON BEAUTY COUPON

$1 OFF

<u>NEW</u> HIDDEN SCENTS
POMANDER
IN CAMPAIGN 15, 1981

Set of three individual ``tulips'' add lovely Meadow Morn fragrance to dresser drawers, pocketbook, suit-case. Beautifully transparent, Hidden Scents is an exclusive creation of the Avon science of hydro-optics.

Return this part to
your Avon Representative

After Shave
Special $2.99
With Coupon: $1.99
Cologne
Special $3.99
With Coupon: $2.99

Return this part to your Avon Representative

Return this part to
your Avon Representative